Find Your Keys

Sara Markos

Illustrated by Dianna Ricotta

ISBN 978-1-63784-088-7 (paperback)
ISBN 978-1-63784-259-1 (hardcover)
ISBN 978-1-63784-089-4 (digital)

Hawes & Jenkins Publishing
16427 N Scottsdale Road Suite 410
Scottsdale, AZ 85254
www.hawesjenkins.com

Printed in the United States of America

To my husband Ted, our amazing children Cate and Pete, and the rest of our large, loud and loving family. Thank you for helping me find my keys. I love you.

All the keys in
the world are
special and unique.

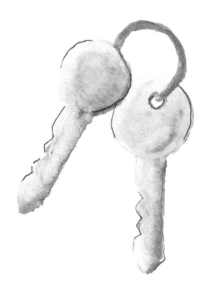

The perfect fit can unlock
what is blocked—but
some can open the door
to SO MUCH MORE.

When you find
one of those
"extra" special keys
it's a powerful
something you
will know is true
because it becomes
part of you.

A curious wonder
fills the air—you
can't help but to
stop and stare.

It brings happy
thoughts to you
on a sad day.

And what is played when
things don't go your way.

It will be there to
lend you courage
as you venture
into the unknown,
all the while you
create a wonderful
path of your own.

And as time passes on and you find yourself lost—know you'll soon be found because your keys bring you home safe and sound.

It is a love to
feel grateful
for every day...

...and brings a calm like the sweetest lullaby song.

It will help teach
the little lessons of
life... all over again.

A positive
attitude.

Patience.

Practice.

And it will tell
you a thousand
stories without
saying one word.

It will help you
reflect on what is
most important—
life's big picture.

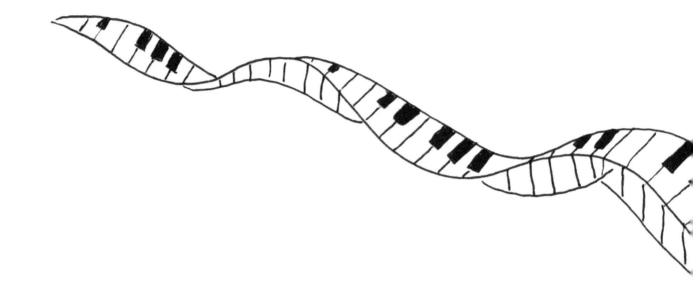

It is a safe place
to go—a place
just for you.

And it is
happy.

So should you ever
lose your keys,
as we sometimes
do, it just means
it's time to get
back to YOU!

Breathe,
slow it down,
and open
your heart
—that is a great way to start.

Rest assured with an attitude of gratitude and a little self-awareness your keys will reveal themselves in the simplest of ways!

Could it be in the **smell**
of fresh cut grass?

"Snip Snap!"

Or in the **sight**
of sparkling blue water?

"Ping!"

It might be the **feel**
of getting squeezed in
a great big bear hug?

"Grrrr!"

What if it is hiding "Slurp!"
in the first **taste**
of a cold
vanilla milkshake!?

"Bum Bum!"

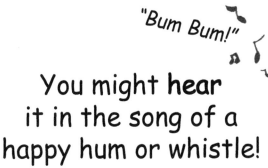

You might **hear**
it in the song of a
happy hum or whistle!

You could find it
in an old memory
tucked away, or in
a new friend just
asking to play.

Remember just like a book—don't judge the look. Every key deserves a try—you might be surprised how it opens your eyes!

So...

What shape are
your keys?

About the Author

Sara Markos lives in Lombard, IL with her husband and two children. When she's not helping in schools as a substitute teacher, you'll find her on the go as a busy hockey mom and lover of all things crafty. Throughout her life she's realized the power of having piano keys to lean on, and the joy it brings her. Sara believes it's important to recognize and appreciate what truly brings you happiness. Now, she's on a mission to help readers young and old find the keys to their happy place.

Printed in the USA
CPSIA information can be obtained
at www.ICGtesting.com
LVHW070557090923
757508LV00003B/78